KS2 national t

Revise wise

Maths

preparation and practice
for use at home

Paul Broadbent
Ann Broadbent

ISBN 0 563 47427 0

Published by BBC Educational Publishing

First Published in 1999

Origination by Sterling

Printed in Great Britain by Sterling

Page Design by Malena Wilson-Max at Tribal Design

Illustrations by Tribal Design

Contents

📺 Means a link to the TV
💿 Means a link to the website

Introduction

What is Key Stage 2 ReviseWise?

In May, Year 6 pupils take their Key Stage 2 (KS2) National Tests in English, Maths and Science. The Tests show teachers what level children are working at to help in their move to secondary school. This book is part of the BBC's Key Stage 2 ReviseWise service, created to help children get ready to do their best in all their KS2 National Tests.

The KS2 ReviseWise Maths resources are:

■ this book

■ television programme that you can video

■ a ready-made video to buy

■ a CD-ROM

■ a website.

The ReviseWise Maths resources have been developed and written by specialists to help children aiming to reach level 4 and above (just over half marks in the Maths Tests will achieve level 4). ReviseWise covers the key areas of Maths which will be tested. The key areas are: using and applying Maths; number; shape, space and measure; and handling data.

If your child uses all the elements of ReviseWise, there's such a variety of things to do that revising need never be boring. There are even ReviseWise resources for schools, so there's a link between home and school learning.

How to get the most out of Key Stage 2 ReviseWise

■ Help your child to work through this book to practise Test-style questions. There are lots of 'Wise-up' tips to help with the answers and give advice.

■ Encourage your child to watch (and re-watch) the video of eight 15-minute sections on key Maths topics. They bring the subject to life and explain what the Tests are all about.

■ Is your child always glued to the computer? The CD-ROM takes children through questions step-by-step, with as much – or as little – help as they need along the way.

■ If you're on the Internet, your child can visit the website for more learning fun. There's also a special section to help parents get to grips with the Tests and revision.

Useful links

There are symbols next to topic headings on the Contents page of this book to show your child where there are links to other parts of the ReviseWise service.

 means a link to the television programme

 means a link to the website

Using this book

Each activity page in this book offers Test-style questions, puzzles or activities which will help children confirm what they know and practise their skills in Maths ready for the KS2 Tests. The main points they need to know are highlighted at the top of each page, followed by the sorts of question-and-answer activities they will meet in the Test. Some things may seem different from when you learned them. Ask your child's teacher if you're not sure.

Children can work steadily through the book, or head straight for the activities they know they need more practice in. At the end of each activity, children can record their progress. They can circle, tick or colour one of these pictures that appear at the side of the page:

 I know this   Come back to this   Ask my teacher

Then it's easy to skim back through the book and see which activities they need to have another go at, or to ask their teacher for a little more help with.

If children do the activities in this book in pencil, they can do them again later, either for repeat practice, or if they get any answers wrong. They can also keep track of how much work they have done by ticking or colouring the shapes on the big ReviseWise Owl at the back of this book.

Answers

The Answers section at the back of this book gives the correct answers to the questions. Questions that are more difficult (level 5) are marked as such next to the answer.

Finally, please remember that the level you feel that your child achieves by answering the questions in this book can only be a general indication of the actual level he or she may achieve in the Tests.

Multiplying and dividing by 10, 100, 1000

Wise up!

When you **multiply** by 100, you move all the digits two places to the left.
Put a zero in the empty places.

× 100

When you multiply, the number gets bigger.
When you divide, the number gets smaller.

When you **divide** by 100, you move all the digits two places to the right.

÷ 100

Remember to remove unnecessary zeros at the end, so 31.20 is just 31.2.

Activities

1 Write the missing numbers in the boxes.

a) 467 × [   ] = 4670

b) 3210 ÷ [   ] = 32.1

c) 96 × 100 = [   ]

*If you multiply by ten, the answer is that number with a zero at the end. But that rule doesn't work for decimals.
3.4 × 10 is not 3.40 it is 34.*

2 Check what these number machines are doing, then write the numbers in the grids. The first ones have been done for you.

IN —— ÷ 10 —— **OUT**

a)

IN	460		1490		5310	640
OUT	46	53		36		

IN —— ÷ 100 —— **OUT**

b)

IN	1100	680		1244		291
OUT	11		975		18	

IN —— × 100 —— **OUT**

c)

IN	4.19	27			5.04	
OUT	419		6200	1900		7500

IN —— × 10 —— **OUT**

d)

IN	42		700			680
OUT	420	370		6200	932	

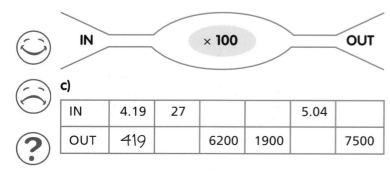
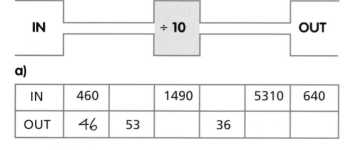
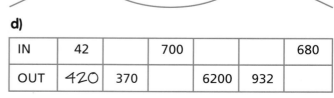

Ordering numbers

Wise up!

When you need to compare large numbers, write them in columns so the units line up. This lets you see which are the largest or smallest numbers. If two numbers are very similar, start at the left and compare the digits in each column for both of them.

Th	H	T	U
4	6	8	3
1	5	9	9
7	0	8	

Start on the left. 708 has no thousands, so it is the smallest number.

Now compare the other two. The one with 1 thousand is smaller than the one with 4 thousands.

Activities

1 Write these three-digit numbers in order, starting with the smallest.

These have the same number of digits, so choose the number with the smallest first digit and put that first. Then choose the next smallest, until all the numbers are sorted.

If any of the numbers have the same first digit, look at the next digit.

Smallest   Largest

2 Follow the path and write < or > between the numbers. Remember: > means "greater than"; < mean "less than".

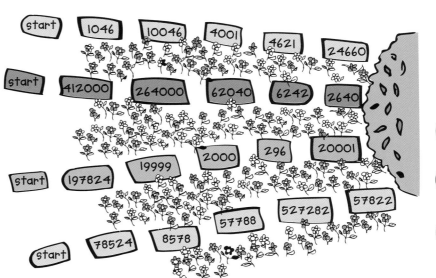

Estimating and rounding numbers

Wise up!

There are three easy ways to round a number:

- to the nearest 10 ⇒ 238 ≈ 240
- to the nearest 100 ⇒ 4614 ≈ 4600
- to the nearest whole number ⇒ 7.6 ≈ 8

Remember a number always sits between two possible answers, you just have to choose which one it is nearest to.

If the number is exactly in the middle (5) or more, round it **up**.

Rounding decimal numbers to the nearest whole number

To round to one decimal place, choose the last digit in the number that you will write.

For example, in 2.75, the number 7 is the last digit to be written (as you are rounding to 1 decimal point).

Now look at the next number to the right. This number – here 5 – is the 'decider' number. The last digit rounds up to 8 because the decider is 5 or more. Answer: 2.8

Activities

1 Round these numbers:

> Ω ≈
> Both these signs mean 'approximately equal to'.

- to the nearest 10   ⇒ 518 ≈ ☐   3672 ≈ ☐
- to the nearest 100   ⇒ 2649 ≈ ☐   5307 ≈ ☐
- to the nearest whole number ⇒ 3.6 ≈ ☐   16.36 ≈ ☐

2 Look at these number lines. Estimate the numbers shown by the arrows. One has been done in each for you.

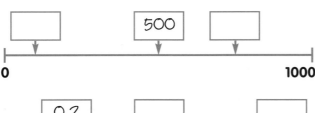

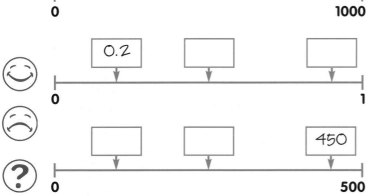

3 Round these numbers to find approximate answers to the sums.

a) 592 + 347   ≈ ☐

b) 1968 + 4091 ≈ ☐

c) 8.2 + 15.75 ≈ ☐

d) 4306 + 198 ≈ ☐

> Estimate is another word for guess. Making estimates helps you to check if your final answer is sensible.

Negative numbers

Wise up!

Sometimes we use numbers less than zero. These are called negative numbers and they have a minus sign in front of them. All the numbers above zero are positive numbers.

Negative numbers occur every day. We use them for cold temperatures such as –10˚C.

A number line is like a big thermometer, listing negative numbers in one direction and positive numbers in the other.

As you go right, the numbers get bigger. As you go left, the numbers get smaller.

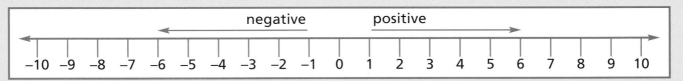

Activities

1 Write the temperatures shown on these thermometers.

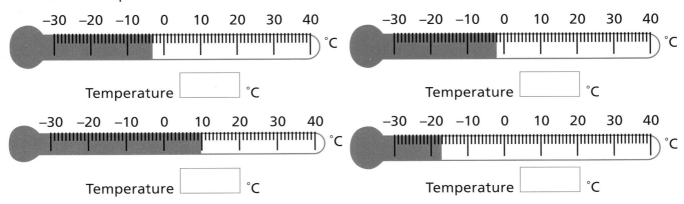

Temperature ☐ ˚C

Temperature ☐ ˚C

Temperature ☐ ˚C

Temperature ☐ ˚C

2 Write the differences between these temperatures.

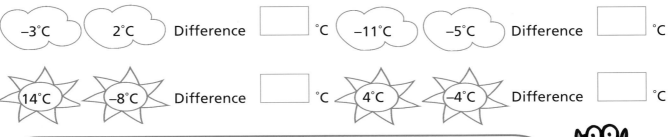

–3˚C   2˚C   Difference ☐ ˚C

–11˚C   –5˚C   Difference ☐ ˚C

14˚C   –8˚C   Difference ☐ ˚C

4˚C   –4˚C   Difference ☐ ˚C

You can use a number line to add and subtract in problems which have negative numbers. You just need to draw part of the number line and then count along to get the answer. When adding, count to the right along the line. When subtracting, count to the left along the line.

Equivalent fractions

Wise up!

Equivalent fractions look different from each other, but are really worth the same.

$$\frac{1}{2} = \frac{2}{4} = \frac{4}{8}$$

$\frac{1}{2}$				$\frac{1}{2}$			
$\frac{1}{4}$		$\frac{1}{4}$		$\frac{1}{4}$		$\frac{1}{4}$	
$\frac{1}{8}$	$\frac{1}{8}$	$\frac{1}{8}$	$\frac{1}{8}$	$\frac{1}{8}$	$\frac{1}{8}$	$\frac{1}{8}$	$\frac{1}{8}$

Our coins are fractions of pounds. For example, two 50 pences are worth the same as five 20 pences, and one 50 pence is worth the same as five 10 pences.

$$\frac{1}{3} = \frac{2}{6} = \frac{4}{12}$$

$\frac{1}{3}$				$\frac{1}{3}$				$\frac{1}{3}$			
$\frac{1}{6}$		$\frac{1}{6}$		$\frac{1}{6}$		$\frac{1}{6}$		$\frac{1}{6}$		$\frac{1}{6}$	
$\frac{1}{12}$	$\frac{1}{12}$	$\frac{1}{12}$	$\frac{1}{12}$	$\frac{1}{12}$	$\frac{1}{12}$	$\frac{1}{12}$	$\frac{1}{12}$	$\frac{1}{12}$	$\frac{1}{12}$	$\frac{1}{12}$	$\frac{1}{12}$

Activities

1 Complete these equivalent fractions.
One has been done for you.

a) $\dfrac{1}{2} = \dfrac{\boxed{}}{10}$

b) $\dfrac{\boxed{5}}{6} = \dfrac{10}{12}$

c) $\dfrac{2}{3} = \dfrac{8}{\boxed{}}$

d) $\dfrac{\boxed{}}{3} = \dfrac{18}{24}$

You can make an equivalent fraction by multiplying or dividing the top and bottom by the same number. In 1 a) 2 × 5 = 10 on the bottom, so 1 × 5 for the top = 5.

2 These pizzas have the same amount left. What is the fraction left for each pizza?

a) $=\dfrac{\boxed{}}{\boxed{}}$ $=\dfrac{\boxed{}}{\boxed{}}$

b) $=\dfrac{\boxed{}}{\boxed{}}$ $=\dfrac{\boxed{}}{\boxed{}}$

3 Circle the odd one out in each box.

a)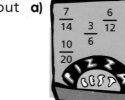
$\dfrac{7}{14}$ $\dfrac{6}{12}$ $\dfrac{4}{8}$
$\dfrac{10}{20}$ $\dfrac{3}{6}$ $\dfrac{5}{15}$

b)
$\dfrac{6}{16}$ $\dfrac{8}{24}$ $\dfrac{12}{32}$
$\dfrac{3}{8}$ $\dfrac{30}{80}$

c)
$\dfrac{18}{20}$ $\dfrac{9}{10}$
$\dfrac{90}{100}$
$\dfrac{40}{50}$ $\dfrac{63}{70}$

Ordering and simplifying fractions

Wise up!

A fraction has two parts.

$\dfrac{3}{4}$ numerator (top number)

    denominator (bottom number)

The numerator tells you how many parts you have. The denominator says how many parts there are in the whole.

Some fractions can be **simplified.**

The numerator and denominator have both been divided by 2.

$$\dfrac{6}{8}\dfrac{(\div 2)}{(\div 2)} \Rightarrow \dfrac{3}{4}$$

When you are **ordering** fractions, change them so they all have the same denominator.

So to order: $\dfrac{1}{2}$ $\dfrac{1}{4}$ $\dfrac{5}{6}$ $\dfrac{2}{3}$

First change them to twelfths. $\Rightarrow$ $\dfrac{6}{12}$ $\dfrac{3}{12}$ $\dfrac{10}{12}$ $\dfrac{8}{12}$

Then order them. $\dfrac{3}{12}$ $\dfrac{6}{12}$ $\dfrac{8}{12}$ $\dfrac{10}{12}$ $\Rightarrow$ $\dfrac{1}{4}$ $\dfrac{1}{2}$ $\dfrac{2}{3}$ $\dfrac{5}{6}$

> If you change the fractions so they have the same denominator, remember that the numerators will change as well.

Activities

1 Write these fractions as simply as possible.

$\dfrac{8}{16} \Rightarrow \boxed{}$ $\dfrac{6}{9} \Rightarrow \boxed{}$ $\dfrac{5}{20} \Rightarrow \boxed{}$ $\dfrac{8}{24} \Rightarrow \boxed{}$ $\dfrac{20}{50} \Rightarrow \boxed{}$ $\dfrac{12}{24} \Rightarrow \boxed{}$

2 Write these fractions in order, starting with the smallest. Here's a clue – you can change them all to the same denominator of 20.

$\dfrac{3}{4}$ $\dfrac{1}{2}$ $\dfrac{3}{5}$ $\dfrac{7}{10}$ $\boxed{}$

3 Write these fractions as simply as possible. The first one has been done for you.

a) $\dfrac{12}{40} \div \dfrac{(\boxed{4})}{(\boxed{4})} = \dfrac{\boxed{3}}{\boxed{10}}$

b) $\dfrac{20}{75} \div \dfrac{(\boxed{})}{(\boxed{})} = \dfrac{\boxed{}}{\boxed{}}$

4 Use any two of these numbers at a time to make fractions of less than 1.

| 8 | 3 | 1 | 6 | 5 |

Write them in order, smallest first.

Improper fractions, mixed numbers

Wise up!

$2\frac{1}{3}$ is a **mixed number** – it has a whole number and a fraction together.

You can change a mixed number into an improper fraction:

$2\frac{1}{3}$ • first change 2 into thirds $\Rightarrow \frac{6}{3}$

• then add $\frac{6}{3}$ and $\frac{1}{3} \Rightarrow \frac{7}{3}$

$\frac{9}{4}$ is an **improper fraction**

You can change an improper fraction into a mixed number:

$\frac{9}{4}$ is the same as $9 \div 4$, which is $2\frac{1}{4}$

Activities

1 Fill in the boxes using these numbers.

| 9 | 15 | 8 | 59 |

a) $1\frac{1}{8} = \dfrac{\boxed{}}{8}$

b) $1\frac{3}{5} = \dfrac{\boxed{}}{5}$

c) $7\frac{1}{2} = \dfrac{\boxed{}}{2}$

d) $5\frac{9}{10} = \dfrac{\boxed{}}{10}$

2 Write these as mixed numbers. The first one has been done for you.

a) $\dfrac{9}{2} = \boxed{4\frac{1}{2}}$

b) $\dfrac{8}{3} = \boxed{}$

c) $\dfrac{11}{4} = \boxed{}$

d) $\dfrac{15}{8} = \boxed{}$

3 Change these whole numbers into improper fractions. Change into thirds.

$6 \Rightarrow \boxed{}$ $4 \Rightarrow \boxed{}$

$10 \Rightarrow \boxed{}$ $7 \Rightarrow \boxed{}$

Change into eighths.

$9 \Rightarrow \boxed{}$ $2 \Rightarrow \boxed{}$

$3 \Rightarrow \boxed{}$ $5 \Rightarrow \boxed{}$

4 Fill in the missing numbers.

a) $\dfrac{\boxed{}}{4} = 2\frac{1}{4}$

b) $\dfrac{11}{\boxed{}} = 3\frac{2}{3}$

c) $\dfrac{20}{9} = \boxed{}\frac{2}{9}$

d) $\dfrac{23}{5} = 4\frac{\boxed{}}{5}$

e) $\dfrac{13}{7} = 1\dfrac{6}{\boxed{}}$

f) $\dfrac{\boxed{}}{2} = 4\frac{1}{2}$

g) $\dfrac{19}{\boxed{}} = 2\frac{3}{8}$

h) $\dfrac{17}{6} = \boxed{}\frac{5}{6}$

Sometimes improper fractions are called "top-heavy" fractions.

Wise up!

It is easy to turn fractions into decimals using a calculator. Just divide the top number by the bottom number.

To change $\frac{1}{2}$ to a decimal, divide 1 by 2 = 0.5.

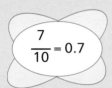
$\frac{7}{10} = 0.7$

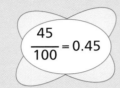
$\frac{45}{100} = 0.45$

Some fractions give recurring decimals.

$\frac{1}{3} \Rightarrow 0.333$ $\frac{1}{6} \Rightarrow 0.1666$

To change decimals into fractions, look at where the last digit after the decimal point is.

So to change 0.23 into a fraction, look at the last digit. It is in the hundredths column, so this would be written as twenty-three hundredths or $\frac{23}{100}$

Activities

1 Write these as decimals.

$\frac{45}{100} =$ ☐ $\frac{3}{100} =$ ☐

$2\frac{3}{4} =$ ☐ $4\frac{7}{10} =$ ☐

$1\frac{1}{5} =$ ☐ $5\frac{3}{4} =$ ☐

2 Write these as fractions.

$0.3 \Rightarrow$ ☐ $0.09 \Rightarrow$ ☐

$0.74 \Rightarrow$ ☐ $0.25 \Rightarrow$ ☐

$0.35 \Rightarrow$ ☐ $0.6 \Rightarrow$ ☐

Look at these examples: 0.7 = seven tenths, 0.36 = thirty-six hundredths, 0.452 = 452 thousandths.

3 Complete this chart by changing the fractions into decimals and the decimals into fractions.

$\frac{1}{4}$			$2\frac{1}{8}$	$1\frac{17}{50}$		$3\frac{1}{5}$		$1\frac{975}{1000}$
	0.7	2.5			1.6		3.47	

4 Use a calculator to change these fractions into decimals. The first one has been done for you. $\frac{7}{8} = 7 \div 8 = 0.875$

$\frac{5}{8} =$ ☐ $\frac{2}{5} =$ ☐

$\frac{7}{9} =$ ☐ $\frac{4}{5} =$ ☐

What do you notice about $\frac{7}{9}$?

Simple percentages

Wise up!

"per cent" means "out of a hundred".

% is a short way of writing per cent. So 60% means "60 out of 100".

This can be written as a fraction: $\dfrac{60}{100}$

Making a percentage into a fraction is easy. You write the percentage as the top number and 100 as the bottom number. So $53\% = \dfrac{53}{100}$

Look at this:

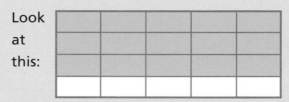

When you are changing a fraction into a percentage, remember that it must be out of 100.

15 out of 20 $\Rightarrow \dfrac{15}{20}$ $\dfrac{15\ (\times 5)}{20\ (\times 5)} = \dfrac{75}{100} \Rightarrow 75\%$

Activities

1 These are Nirmal's marks in his spelling tests. Change them all to percentages. (Remember to make them out of 100.)

9 out of 10 $\Rightarrow$ ⬚ %

18 out of 25 $\Rightarrow$ ⬚ %

37 out of 50 $\Rightarrow$ ⬚ %

You can use percentages to make it easier to compare fractions.

For example, which is bigger, $\dfrac{4}{5}$ or $\dfrac{3}{4}$?

$\dfrac{4}{5} = 80\%$ and $\dfrac{3}{4} = 75\%$

Now you can see that $\dfrac{4}{5}$ is bigger.

His best score was ⬚ out of ⬚

2 What percentage of each of these shapes is shaded? The fraction is given for you.

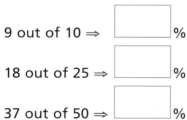
$\dfrac{1}{2}$ ⬚

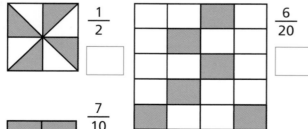
$\dfrac{6}{20}$ ⬚

$\dfrac{7}{10}$ ⬚

$\dfrac{1}{4}$ ⬚

3 Write these fractions as percentages.

a) $\dfrac{3}{10} = $ ⬚ %

b) $\dfrac{11}{20} = $ ⬚ %

c) $\dfrac{2}{5} = $ ⬚ %

d) $\dfrac{45}{50} = $ ⬚ %

4 Write these as simple fractions.

a) $60\% = $ ⬚

b) $35\% = $ ⬚

c) $95\% = $ ⬚

d) $18\% = $ ⬚

Fractions, decimals and percentages

Wise up!

There are some fractions, decimals and percentages that we use a lot. It's a good idea to try to learn these so that you can convert from one to another instantly in your head. Here are the main ones to learn:

Fraction	$\frac{1}{2}$	$\frac{1}{4}$	$\frac{3}{4}$	$\frac{1}{5}$	$\frac{1}{10}$
Decimal	0.5	0.25	0.75	0.2	0.1
Percentage	50%	25%	75%	20%	10%

 $\frac{1}{4} = 0.25 = 25\%$

Here are the calculations you need to know to change decimals to fractions and percentages and back again.

- To change decimals to % ⇒ × 100
  e.g. 0.4 = 0.4 × 100 = 40%
- To change % to decimals ⇒ ÷ 100
  e.g. 5% = 5 ÷ 100 = 0.05
- to change fractions to % ⇒ make the fraction 'out of 100', e.g.
  $$\frac{4}{5} = \frac{(× 20)}{(× 20)} = \frac{80}{100} = 80\%$$
- To change % to fractions ⇒ make a % out of 100 and simplify, e.g. 70% = $\frac{70}{100} = \frac{7}{10}$

Activities

1 Write the rest of the missing digits.

$\frac{3}{5}$ = 0.6 = ☐ % $\frac{3}{4}$ = 0.☐ = 75%

2 Circle each number that is less than 33%

| 0.1 | 0.5 | 30% | $\frac{1}{2}$ | 20% |

When you compare fractions, decimals and percentages, remember that 100% is the same as 1 whole. > means greater than and < means less than.

3 Change these percentages into decimals.

60% = ☐   75% = ☐   32% = ☐

4 Write these decimals as percentages.

0.4 ⇒ ☐ %   0.33 ⇒ ☐ %   0.08 ⇒ ☐ %   0.85 ⇒ ☐ %

% to decimals = divide by 100; decimals to % = multiply by 100

Percentages of quantities

Wise up!

To find a percentage of a number, you need to turn it into a decimal first and then turn it into a percentage.

So to find 15% of 60, first convert 15% to a decimal (0.15) and then use your calculator to work out 0.15 × 60 = 9

It is useful to know how to find 1% and 10%.

1% of 300 is 3

so

2% of 300 is 6
3% of 300 is 9
4% of 300 is 12

10% of 60 is 6

so

5% of 60 is 3
20% of 60 is 12
30% of 60 is 18

Activities

1 Work out these amounts.

   a) 30% of 80 = ☐

   b) 25% of 400 = ☐

3 The price of a bike is £140.
There is 40% off in the sale.
How much will the bike cost in the sale?

£ ☐

4 When Mrs Potts went shopping, she found that the weights of all her favourite cereals had been changed.
Write the new weights in the chart.

2 This glass holds 500ml of an orange drink, 75% is water and 25% is squash.

How much is:

water? ☐ ml

squash? ☐ ml

Some words have special meanings in maths. When you see 'of', it usually means you are going to have to multiply something.

Here's a clue. First work out the extra percentage and then add that to the original weight. So 30% of 370g = 111g, add that to 370g = 481g.

Cereal	Weight	New weight (30% extra)
Honeycrunch	370g	
Choc Pops	400g	
Crisp Flakes	280g	
Bran Bites	420g	
Oat Ovals	450g	

Mental addition

Wise up!

Numbers can be added in any order.

$36 + 83 = 83 + 36$

$25 + 94 = 94 + 25$

Use the order you find easiest.

Breaking up numbers into smaller sums can help you add numbers mentally.

$58 + 37$ is the same as

$58 + 30 + 7 \Rightarrow 88 + 7$

which is 95

Rounding numbers can be helpful.

$54 + 79$ is the same as

$54 + 80 - 1 = 134 - 1 = 133$

$67 + 52$ is the same as

$67 + 50 + 2 = 117 + 2 = 119$

Activities

1 Make a total of 110 in three different ways, using only these numbers.

 2 8 6 4

☐☐ + ☐☐ = 110

☐☐ + ☐☐ = 110

☐☐ + ☐☐ = 110

2 Write the missing numbers.

a) 2 + ☐ = 17   **b)** 55 + 33 = ☐

c) 30 + ☐ = 94   **d)** 43 + 91 = ☐

Sometimes it helps to put the bigger number first. Do you know any other ways to make adding easier?

3 Complete the number clues in the box and then fill in the answers on the grid.

Across		Down	
A	24 + 25	A	29 + 12
C	58 + 23	B	45 + 47
D	12 + 15	C	66 + 16
F	19 + 13	E	38 + 37
G	46 + 22		
H	37 + 16		

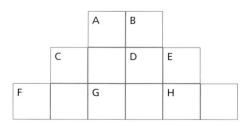

4 Complete these addition walls. The first one has been done for you.

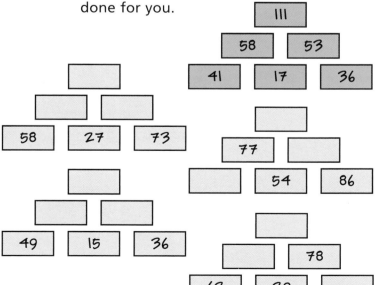

Adding 3-digit numbers

Wise up!

You can add numbers quickly using a calculator, but it is good to know how to add mentally and on paper. Here are three different ways to add.

 360 + 165

Rounding numbers is a good way to add in your head. For this sum, 360 add 160 is 520, add 5 is 525

254 + 135

Counting on is a way of working out the difference by holding numbers in your head and counting in steps. For this sum, 200 add 100 is 300, 50 add 30 is 80, 4 add 5 is 9, so 300 + 80 + 9 = 389

 574 + 387

Sometimes, for larger numbers, it is easier to write the sum down. Remember to line up the hundreds, tens and units!

To answer this sum you write:

```
   574
 + 387
 -----
   961
   1 1
```

Activities

1 Add the numbers and write the totals in the boxes.

a)   314 + 120 = ☐

b)   273 + 560 = ☐

c)   480 + 118 = ☐

2 Circle the two numbers that total 295.

102   125   206   170

> When you use a mental method, you work out the answer 'in your head'. You need to be able to do this a lot, in maths, so practise when you can.

3 Find the numbers hidden by the stars.

a)
```
  ★72
+ 20
----
 292
```

b)
```
 631
+ 187
----
★18
```

c)
```
 255
+ 273
----
★28
```

4 Mr Block lays wooden floors. He is sorting out his offcuts and trying to make up useful lengths. Look at these pairs of blocks and work out their total length.

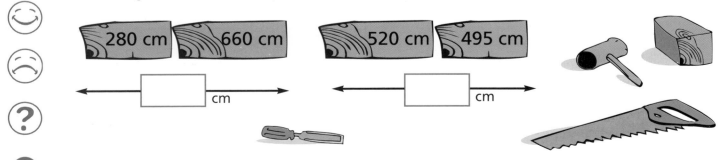

280 cm   660 cm   520 cm   495 cm

☐ cm   ☐ cm

Adding large numbers

Wise up!

Adding large numbers seems tricky, but if you follow these steps, you'll soon get used to it.

- Write the numbers on top of one another. Remember to line up the units.
- Add the units column first. Then add the tens and then the hundreds.
- If one of the columns adds up to 10 or more, place the right digit of the answer in

that column and carry over the left digit to the column on the left.

| 48 + 759 + 247 |

```
        48
       759
    +  247
    ------
      1054
      1 12
```

Activities

1 Find the total of these three numbers.

428   135   90   Total [   ]

Show your working.

[   ]

When you are adding more than two numbers, it can be helpful to write the biggest number first.

2  4560   315   250   1262

- Make the largest possible total you can from any two of these numbers.

  [   ]

- Now make the smallest possible total from any two of these numbers.

  [   ]

These sums are difficult, see if you can work them out.

3 These are the sales figures for an ice cream van on a bank holiday weekend. Complete the chart.

Flavour	Sat	Sun	Mon	Total
Vanilla	430	1655	2086	
Strawberry	592	1917	1775	
Chocolate	628	1893	2434	
Total				

4 Answer these.

a)
```
    153
  + 749
  -----
```

b)
```
   8806
 + 7395
 ------
```

c)
```
  15 120
+ 78 947
--------
```

d)
```
  29 568
+ 33 462
--------
```

Adding decimals

Wise up!

Adding decimals is just like normal number sums. You just need to remember where to put the decimal point.

If the numbers are small, you can add them in your head by breaking them up into smaller chunks: 4.2 + 3.6 is 4.2 + 3 = 7.2, add another 0.6 = 7.8

If you have a few numbers to add, you can write them in columns, like this:

Remember to line up the decimal point and, if the question is about money, make sure the pound sign goes in the answer.

```
    4.68
   27.04
+ 173.9
  205.62
   11 1 1
```

Activities

1 Circle the two numbers that total **30.5**

| 16.1 | 27.4 | 14.4 | 12.6 |

2 Work out the number that is hidden under the star. Write the sum out in full.

```
   13.5
+ ★1.6
   55.1
```

3 How much do the combinations of musical things listed below the pictures cost?

£152.50

£8.40

£14.95

£78.60

£6.45

When totalling money or measures, line up the units and the decimal points.

- trumpet + music stand + book   £ [ ]

 - recorder + book   £ [ ]

 - guitar + trumpet + recorder   £ [ ]

 - guitar + book + stand   £ [ ]

4 One decimal point is missing in each of these sums.

Rewrite the questions with the decimal points in the correct places.

4.6 + 1103 = 15.63   [ ]

57.8 + 295 = 60.75   [ ]

10.62 + 3.04 = 1366   [ ]

Mental subtraction

Wise up!

It is not always possible to write down maths calculations. For example, when you are paying for things in a shop or deciding what you can afford, you have to work out the maths in your head. Here are two ways to work out $93 - 58$ in your head.

a Breaking up numbers into smaller chunks can help when you have to subtract mentally.

For 93 – 58, you can use one of these methods:

> 93 subtract 50 is 43, take away another 8 is 35.

> 93 take away 60 is 33. Add 2 is 35.

b Counting on is a good way of subtracting. For 93 – 58, first count on from 58 to 60. Hold 2 in your head. Count on to 93 which is 33. Add 2 to 33, which is 35.

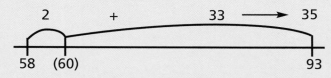

Activities

1 Find the differences between these prices.

The key words in subtraction are subtract, minus, difference and less than.

a) 62p 40p difference: ☐ p

b) 94p 62p difference: ☐ p

2 Use these numbers.

22	60	78	85

■ Which two numbers have a difference of 18?

☐ and ☐

■ Which two numbers have a difference of 56?

☐ and ☐

■ Find the difference between 92 and each of the numbers. Which number gives:

☆ the greatest difference? ☐

☆ the smallest difference? ☐

Remember to check your answers using inverse addition: 92 – 22 = 70, so 70 + 22 = 92!

Subtracting 3-digit numbers

Wise up!

Subtraction is another word for 'taking away' or 'difference'. You can subtract very quickly using a calculator, but it is good to know how to subtract mentally or on paper. Here are the three different ways to subtract.

> When you are asked to find the difference, take the smaller number away from the bigger number.

174 − 129

Rounding numbers is a good way to subtract in your head. For this sum, 174 − 130 is 44, add 1 is 45.

206 − 185

Counting on is a way of working out the difference by holding numbers in your head and counting in steps. For this sum, 185 counting on to 200 is 15, count on a further 6 is 21.

463 − 287

Sometimes, for larger numbers, it is easier to write the sum down. Rememer to line up the hundreds, tens and units! To answer this sum you write:

$$
\begin{array}{r}
{}^{3}\cancel{4}\ \ {}^{15}\cancel{6}\ \ {}^{13}\cancel{3} \\
-\ 2\ \ \ \ 8\ \ \ \ 7 \\
\hline
1\ \ \ \ 7\ \ \ \ 6 \\
\hline
\end{array}
$$

Activities

1 a) 490 − 300 = ☐

b) 508 − 218 = ☐

2 Which two of these numbers have a difference of **158**?

☐ | 531 | 689 | 475

3 Follow the paths and subtract to find the missing numbers. You can try to work them out mentally or you can write them down on a separate piece of paper.

a)
Start 950 → − 130 → ☐ → − 200 → ☐

b)
612 Start − 245 ☐ − 291 ☐

c)
612 Start − 310 ☐ − 50 ☐

Subtracting large numbers

Wise up!

You can subtract large numbers using a calculator, but it is good to know how to do it on paper. Here are two ways to subtract large numbers.

a Decomposition

Write the biggest number on top and line the units up. Subtract the units column, then the tens, the hundreds, and the thousands.

$^6\cancel{7}\,^{12}\cancel{2}\,^2\cancel{3}\,^{18}\cancel{8}$
$-\,2\,\,7\,\,1\,\,9$
$\overline{4\,\,5\,\,1\,\,9}$

Borrowing: If a column has a smaller digit on top, the digit on top borrows from the digit to its left.

b Complementary addition

$$7238$$
$$-\,2719$$

81 (Counting on to 2800)
200 (Counting on to 3000)
4238 (Counting on to 7238)
_____
4519

Activities

1 What is the difference in the weights of these two parcels? [____] g

Show your working.

[ ]

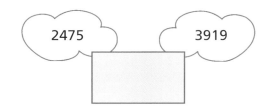

Always show your working if you are asked. It helps you – or an adult – to see if you have made a simple mistake. You may still get marks for your method.

2 Write the answers in this number puzzle.

A		B	
C			
	D		E
F			
G			

Across
A 4700 – 2061
C 8936 – 3535
F 9214 – 2107
G 7264 – 5579
Down
A 9230 – 6280
B 9030 – 5526
D 10 000 – 1864
E 4301 – 2516

3 Find the difference between these two numbers.

2475   3919

[ ]

Subtracting decimals

Wise up!

Subtracting decimals is just like subtracting whole numbers – you just have to remember to line up the decimal points.

To work out $173.8 - 56.9$

Write the biggest number on top, and line the units up.

Subtract the tenths column, then the units, then the tens, then the hundreds.

$$
\begin{array}{r}
1\ {}^6\!\!\not{7}\ {}^{12}\!\!\not{3}\ .\ {}^{18}\!\!\not{8} \\
-\quad 5\ 6\ .\ 9 \\
\hline
1\ 1\ 6\ .\ 9
\end{array}
$$

Activities

1 How much has the price of each bike been reduced by?

a) Was £210.90

New price £183.50

Saving £ ⬚

b) Was £156.45

New price £89.90

Saving £ ⬚

2 Circle the two numbers with a difference of 13.6

| 23.8 | 16.6 | 10.2 |

In problems involving money, remember to use a pound sign in the answer. Always estimate an approximate answer first, then you can check that your exact answer is sensible.

3 Write the missing prices in this sales chart. The first one has been done for you.

Model	Tricycle	BMX bike	Mountain bike	Racer	Shopper
Was	£27.50	£49.90	£91.35	£86.50	£42.30
Now	£18.55	£36.00		£79.25	
Saving	£8.95		£25.50		£9.25

4 A decimal point is missing in each of these sums.
Rewrite the sums with the decimal points in the correct places.

a) $5.32 - 1.85 = 347$ ⬚

b) $14.52 - 939 = 5.13$ ⬚

The decimal point shows where the whole number ends and the decimal part begins.

c) $20.6 - 2.06 = 1854$ ⬚

Multiplication: TU x U

Wise up!

Multiplying by a single digit number is easy if you know your times tables. You multiply the single digit by each digit of the big number in turn. You can start with the tens and then work out the units and then add them together. Or you can work out the units first, then the tens.

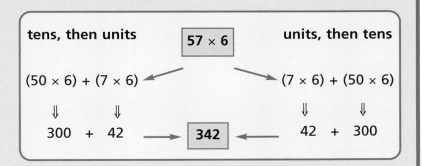

tens, then units 57×6 units, then tens

$(50 \times 6) + (7 \times 6)$ ⟵   ⟶ $(7 \times 6) + (50 \times 6)$

⇓   ⇓   ⇓   ⇓

$300 + 42$ ⟶ 342 ⟵ $42 + 300$

Activities

1 Circle the calculation with the answer that is nearest to 300.

98×3 71×4 52×6

2 A chocolate bar weighs 37g. How much do six chocolate bars weigh? [   ] g

Show your working.

Make sure you know all your times tables up to "10 times 10 is 100".

So if one yoghurt weighs 48g, six yoghurts weigh $6 \times 48 = 288g$.

3 Write the total weights for each of these multi-buys.

a) 6 yoghurts   [   ] g

b) 4 tins of beans   [   ] g

c) 8 boxes of cereal   [   ] g

d) 3 packets of biscuits   [   ] g

48g each

90g each

73g each   89g each

biscuits   biscuits

Multiplying large numbers

Wise up!

Large numbers are difficult to multiply.

Here are two ways to work out multiplication sums with large numbers.

Use the method you find easiest.

a Grid method

Break up the large number into hundreds, tens and units. Multiply each separately and then add the answers together.

×	500	20	8
6	3000	120	48

(3000 + 120 + 48)

To work out:
528 × 6

⇒

So the answer is 3168

⇐

b Vertical method

Write the sum like this. Make sure you line up the units, tens and hundreds underneath each other.

```
     528
   ×   6
   ─────
    3168
      14
```

Activities

1 A box holds 483 sheets of paper.
Work out how many sheets of paper there are in:

3 boxes [　　] 　 7 boxes [　　]

8 boxes [　　] 　 4 boxes [　　]

 These questions need some juggling of big numbers. Remember that a product is the answer to a multiplication sum.

2 Answer these.
Work them out on a separate piece of paper.

147 × 8 = [　　] 　 310 × 2 = [　　]

622 × 7 = [　　] 　 581 × 3 = [　　]

496 × 4 = [　　] 　 270 × 9 = [　　]

859 × 2 = [　　] 　 334 × 6 = [　　]

3 Sam was playing with these number cards.

[2] [8] [7] [4]

He made multiplication sums, like this.

- What is the largest possible product?

[　　]

- What is the smallest possible product?

[　　]

Wise up! | 47 × 36 |

A long multiplication sum like this looks difficult because you don't have a single-digit number to multiply by. To make it easier split the number into tens and units and use the grid method:

×	40	7	
30	1200	210	⇒ 1410
6	240	42	⇒ 286

1692

The other way of working out the long multiplication sum 47 × 36 is to work out 47 × 6 and 47 × 30 and then add the answers up.

Ignore the 3 and treat it as 47 × 6 ⟶

Now ignore the 6 and treat it as 47 × 30

Add them up to get the final answer.

```
    47
 ×  36
   282
  1410
  1692
```

Activities

1 This is the plan of a school hall. Work out the area of the floor.

23m

14m

Show your working.

area = [   ] m²

2 Mr Lee saves £85 each month. How much does he save in a year? (Remember there are 12 months in a year!)

Show your working.

£ [   ]

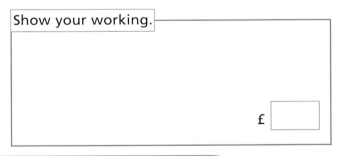

The area of a rectangle is length x breadth. The answer will always be squared (²).

3 Use these cards to make different multiplication sums.

[ ] [ ] [ ]

× [ ]

■ Find the largest possible product. [   ]

■ Find the smallest possible product. [   ]

4 Calculate the area of these gardens.

41m

19m

area = [   ] m²

37m

28m

area = [   ] m²

Multiplying decimals

Multiplying decimals is like multiplying whole numbers – you just have to make sure that the decimal points are lined up.

Multiply the single digit number by each digit of the decimal number in turn. Start with the hundredths, then tenths, then units and so on.

$$
\begin{array}{r}
34.67 \\
\times \quad 4 \\
\hline
138.68 \\
\hline
1\ 2\ 2
\end{array}
$$

If you get an answer of 10 or more, carry the left digit of the answer to the next column.

Always estimate an approximate answer first: 34.67 × 4 is approximately 4 × 35, which is 140.

Activities

1 A litre of petrol costs £0.70. What is the cost of 30 litres of petrol?   £ ☐

2 A loaf of bread weighs 0.8 kg. How much do six loaves of bread weigh? ☐ kg

3 Calculate 15.7 × 2

Show your working.

4 Steven has started to work out these sums. Help him by finishing the estimates. Then work out the actual answers.

	Estimate	Answer
11.3 × 5 =	11 × 5 = 55	☐
6.7 × 7 =	7 × 7 = 49	☐
2.6 × 3 =	☐	☐
7.45 × 8 =	☐	☐

5 Write the numbers that come out of these machines.

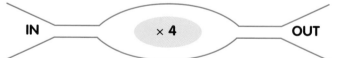

IN	4.6	3.9	12.8	0.5	16.1	0.7
OUT						

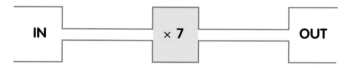

IN	2.14	5.08	10.72	13.95	0.06	7.09
OUT						

Check your answers with a calculator. How accurate were you? Are your estimates close?

Division: TU ÷ U

Wise up!

51 ÷ 3 can be written as 3⟌51

To work out this sum, divide into 51 one digit at a time, starting from the left (the 5). Put the result of each division on top of the line.

$$\frac{1\ 7}{3\overline{\smash{)}5\,^21}}$$

Remember: if the small number won't go into the large number exactly, carry the remainder across (to the next digit on the right).

Multiplication and division are opposites or "inverses". You can check the answer to a division question by turning it into a multiplication one.

3 × 6 = 18   [18] ÷ 6 = 3

Activities

1 92 children are divided into 4 classes? How many children are in each class? [ ]

Show your working.

2 Write the missing number.

78 ÷ 3 = [ ]

3 A photo album holds 96 photos. There are six photos to a page. How many pages are there?

[ ] pages

4 Write the missing numbers.

a) 12 ÷ 4 = [ ]

b) $\frac{56}{7}$ = [ ]

c) [ ] ÷ 3 = 16

d) [ ]
   5⟌95

e)   29
   2⟌[ ]

f) [ ]
   6⟌78

5   82   55   49   93

- Which of these numbers can be divided exactly by 2? [ ]

- Which of these numbers can be divided exactly by 7? [ ]

There are different ways to describe division. 12 divided by 4, 12 shared by 4 and 4 into 12 are all ways of saying the same thing. You can write them in different ways too:

$\frac{12}{4}$ 12 ÷ 4   4⟌12

Long division: HTU ÷ TU

Wise up!

Always estimate an approximate answer first, then check that the exact answer is sensible. For 774 ÷ 18, the estimate will be:

800 ÷ 20 = 40

Remember that multiplication and division are opposites or "inverses". If you multiply by an amount and then divide by the same amount, you end up back where you started.

$$774 \div 18$$

The big number goes inside.

```
      43
 18⟌774
    720      ⇒ (18 × 40 = 720)
   ─────
     54
     54      ⇒ (18 × 3 = 54)
   ─────
      0
```

Activities

1 Find the numbers hidden by the stars.

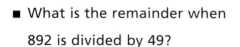

```
       2 9
 34⟌★★★
```

Show your working.

2 A piece of string is 145cm long.

■ How many 28cm lengths can be cut from it? ☐

■ How long is the piece left over? ☐ cm

Show your working.

3 Calculate the answers to these. Remember to estimate first.

■ Divide 315 by 45. ☐

■ What is the remainder when 892 is divided by 49? ☐

■ Share 972 equally among 27. ☐

■ What is left over when 763 is shared by 38? ☐

4 Mrs Jones is saving up for a holiday. The total cost is £675. She can save £27 a week. How many weeks will it take her to save up for her holiday? ☐

In long division, keep the numbers in their columns and bring down the next number. If it "won't go", write a zero on the top line and bring down the next number. Don't forget to put those zeros in, or your answer will be wrong.

Single-stage problems

Wise up!

Single-stage problems just need one calculation to find the answer. It might be an addition, a subtraction, a multiplication or a division question. Practise spotting what type of sum you need to do. Make sure you think about these four steps for solving problems.

| 1 Read the problem. | → | 2 Organise the calculation. | → | 3 Answer the calculation. | → | 4 Answer the problem. |

Activities

1 Caroline has 36 stick insects. She puts them in equal numbers into three tanks. How many does she put in each tank? ☐

Show your working.

2 David has £40 more in his bank account than Hannah, who has £122.
How much does David have in his account?

£ ☐

It is important that you show your working out. You may get a mark for showing your method.

3 Ranjit's school collected cans.

Collect a can	
Class	Number of cans
Class 6	432
Class 5	389
Class 4	415

- How many cans did Class 6 and Class 5 collect together? ☐
- How many more cans did Class 4 collect than Class 5? ☐

4 These are the prices in a pet shop.

£3.60   £4.30

£8.70   £0.89

Find the total price of:
- a dog collar and a bowl   £ ☐
- six bones   £ ☐
- one tin of dog food   £ ☐

If you bought the dog collar, how much change would you get from £10? £ ☐

Two-stage problems

Wise up!

Two-stage problems need two separate calculations to find the answer. Read the problem carefully to see what you are being asked to do.

Can you make it easier by breaking the calculations into smaller chunks?

Make sure you think about these four steps for solving problems.

| 1 Read the problem. | → | 2 Organise the two calculations. | → | 3 Answer the calculations. | → | 4 Answer the problem. |

Activities

1 Mr Potts, the chemist, pours 365ml of formula X liquid into a jug and tops it up with 160ml of water. The mixture is poured equally into five bottles. How much is there in each bottle?

_____ ml

Show your working.

2 Anna buys four plants at 50p each. How much change will she get from £5?

£ _____

3 Tom reads 12 pages of his book every night. How many pages will he have read in three weeks? (Here's a clue: there are 7 nights in a week, so there are 21 nights in 3 weeks.)

_____ pages

4 Six bags of crisps cost £1.68. How much would five bags of crisps cost? (First you need to work out what one bag of crisps costs and then times that by 5.)

£ _____

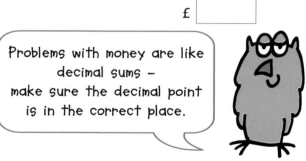

Problems with money are like decimal sums – make sure the decimal point is in the correct place.

5 Swimming: Adults   £2.50

                    Children   £1.85

How much would it cost for these groups?

- 2 adults and 1 child   £ _____

- 1 adult and 3 children   £ _____

- If you buy a ten-visit child ticket, you save £1.50. How much will a ten-visit child ticket cost?

£ _____

Three-stage problems

Wise up!

Three-stage problems need three separate calculations to find the answer. Read the problem carefully to see what you are being asked to do.

Try to make it easier by breaking the calculations into three separate stages. Make sure you show your working, as you can get marks for getting some of the stages right.

| 1 Read the problem. | → | 2 Organise the three calculations. | → | 3 Answer the calculations. | → | 4 Answer the problem. |

Activities

1 How long is 792 hours, in weeks and days?

Show your working.

Remember: there are 24 hours in a day and 7 days in a week.

2 Mark is training for the London Marathon. He runs 90 miles a week. He runs the same distance every day, but he does not run on Sundays. How far does he run on a Thursday? (Here's a clue: first work out the number of days he goes running, then divide the total miles for the week by the number of days.)

 miles

Mark increases the total he runs in a week to 120 miles. How many miles does he now run each day?

 miles

3 Mrs Smith buys four pots of paint at £4 and ten rolls of wallpaper at £9.
How much does she spend in total?

£

Long distances are sometimes measured in miles instead of metres and kilometres. Practise using imperial measurements, such as miles.

Problem-solving

Wise up!

In the test, instead of being given some numbers and told to add or subtract them, you might be given some real life situations. You will have to spot whether these are addition, subtraction, multiplication or division problems.

Try to picture the problem in your mind and work out what calculations you need to do.

| 1 Read the problem. | → | 2 Organise the calculations. | → | 3 Answer the calculations. | → | 4 Answer the problem. |

Activities

1 Peter can swim 25m in 30 seconds. How far can he swim in six minutes going at the same speed?

Show your working.

It is important that you show your working out. You may get a mark for showing your method. (Did you know that there are 60 seconds in a minute?)

2 A dressmaker has a piece of fabric 5670mm long.

■ If she cuts it into nine equal lengths, how long will each piece be?

◻ mm

■ If she cuts off 4 metres, how much will be left? (A clue: 4 metres is 4000mm.)

◻ mm

■ If she cuts it into thirds, what will the length of each piece be?

◻ mm

3 Apples are 25p each. Mrs Hogg has £1.25. How many apples can she buy?

◻

4 Amy's rabbit weighed 500g when she bought it six weeks ago. It gained 50g per week for four weeks, then 10g in the next two weeks. How heavy is it now?

◻ g

Try making up some word problems about things around you – such as football scores or prices at the shops. You could ask a friend to solve them.

Mental maths: adding and subtracting

Wise up!

It's good to know some quick ways of adding and subtracting numbers in your head. The sum 62 + 9 might look tricky, but it's easier if you break it up into two sums. Adding 9 is the same as adding 10 and then taking away 1. So 62 + 10 = 72, 72 - 1 = 71.

To add 9 Add 10 subtract 1	To add 11 Add 10 add 1	To subtract 9 Subtract 10 add 1	To add 0.9 Add 1 subtract 0.1	To subtract 0.9 Subtract 1 add 0.1
To add 19 Add 20 subtract 1	To add 21 Add 20 add 1	To subtract 19 Subtract 20 add 1	To add 1.9 Add 2 subtract 0.1	To subtract 1.9 Subtract 2 add 0.1
$86 + 10 - 1 = 95$	$67 + 10 + 1 = 78$	$38 - 10 + 1 = 29$	$6.3 + 1 - 0.1 = 7.2$	$7.4 - 1 + 0.1 = 6.5$
$74 + 20 - 1 = 93$	$58 + 20 + 1 = 79$	$63 - 20 + 1 = 44$	$18.5 + 2 - 0.1 = 20.4$	$9.6 - 2 + 0.1 = 7.7$

Activities

1 What is the difference in weight between these two parcels? [ ] kg

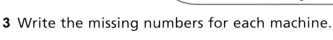

2 Write the missing numbers.

a) $47 + 29 =$ [ ]

b) $0.6 + 0.9 =$ [ ]

c) $72 - 9 =$ [ ]

d) $4.9 + 1.9 =$ [ ]

To work out 45 − 13, break it into two easy sums. Subtracting 13 is the same as subtracting 10 and then subtracting 3: 45 − 10 = 35, 35 − 3 = 32!

3 Write the missing numbers for each machine.

a)
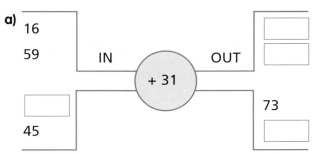

16
59
IN   + 31   OUT [ ] [ ]
[ ]
45   73

b)
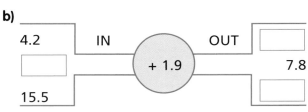

4.2   IN   OUT [ ]
[ ]   + 1.9   7.8
15.5   [ ]

c)
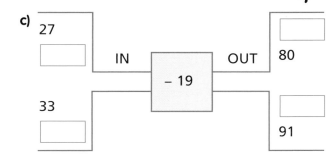

27
[ ]   IN   − 19   OUT [ ]   80
33   [ ]   91

d)
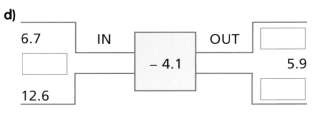

6.7   IN   OUT [ ]
[ ]   − 4.1   5.9
12.6   [ ]

Mental maths: using doubles

Wise up!

Numbers that are the same are easy to add up in your head. These numbers are called "doubles". So in the sum 37 + 37 = 74 you are adding doubles.

Sometimes you have to add numbers that are almost the same – these numbers are called "near-doubles". In the sum 37 + 38 you are adding near doubles. It is easier to work out if you think of the doubles sum first: 37 + 37 = 74, add 1 = 75.

Look at these. Do you see how they have been worked out?

1.8 + 1.8 = 3.6

1.8 + 1.9 = 3.7

0.18 + 0.19 = 0.37

52 and 53 are near doubles, so are 0.5 and 0.4. Can you think of some more near doubles?

Activities

1 Write the answers.

a) double 46

b) 5.3 + 5.3

c) 270 × 2

d) double 9

2 Answer these.

a) 8 + 7 =

b) 10.4 + 10.5 =

c) 32 + 33 =

d) 198 + 203 =

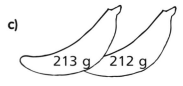

Did you notice that doubling is the same as multiplying by 2?

3 Write the total weight for each pair.

a)

173 g   174 g

Total

b)

249 g   251 g

Total

c)

213 g   212 g

Total

d)

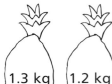

1.3 kg   1.2 kg

Total

e)

27 g   25 g

Total

f)

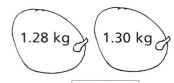

1.28 kg   1.30 kg

Total

Mental maths: counting on

Wise up!

It is not always possible to write down maths calculations. For example, when you are paying for things in a shop, you have to work out the maths in your head. Counting on is a good way to subtract in your head. It uses a number line to count in stages, as shown on the right.

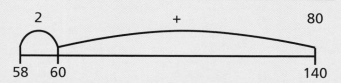

To find the difference between 58 and 140

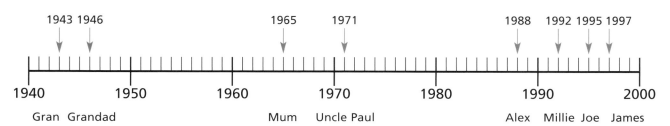

First count on from 58 to 60. Hold 2 in your head. Count on to 140 which is 80. Add 2 to 80 which is 82.

Activities

1 This number line shows the years in which members of Millie's family were born.

1943 1946   1965   1971   1988 1992 1995 1997

1940   1950   1960   1970   1980   1990   2000

Gran Grandad   Mum   Uncle Paul   Alex   Millie Joe   James

Find the difference in age to the nearest year between:

■ Grandad and Gran [   ] years

■ Alex and Joe [   ] years

■ Grandad and Millie [   ] years

Practise using number lines. Remember that the further right you go, the higher the number and the further left you go, the lower the number.

2 Find the difference between the numbers in each pair.

a) 73 and 103 [   ]

b) 48 and 60 [   ]

c) 95 and 310 [   ]

d) 236 and 507 [   ]

3 Every work day, Mrs Butler bought a sandwich from the canteen. Write down how much change she got each day from £5.

Day	Cost	Change from £5
Monday	£3.50	
Tuesday	£2.05	
Wednesday	£1.60	
Thursday	£0.99	
Friday	£2.20	

Mental maths: inverses

Wise up!

When you subtract an amount and then add the same amount, you end up back where you started. This is because subtraction and addition are opposites or "inverses".

If you multiply by an amount and then divide by the same amount, you end up where you started, because multiplication and division are also opposites.

Always check your answers using opposites.

You can check a subtraction by adding.

$78 - 49 = 29$

$29 + 49 = 78$

You can check a division by multiplying.

$72 \div 3 = 24$

$24 \times 3 = 72$

Activities

1 Write the missing numbers in the boxes.

$36 - 14 = \boxed{}$

$14 + \boxed{} = 36$

$31 + 64 = \boxed{}$

$\boxed{} - 64 = 31$

So if you add 64, you can check the answer by taking away 64. This will leave you with the number you started with. Practise checking calculations by carrying out the opposite.

2 Complete these number machines.

a)

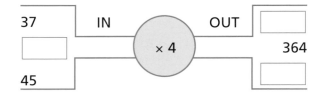

37	IN	OUT	
	×4	364
45		

b)

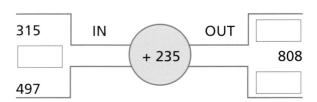

315	IN	OUT	
	+ 235	808
497		

c)

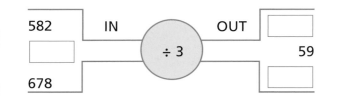

582	IN	OUT	
	÷ 3	59
678		

d)

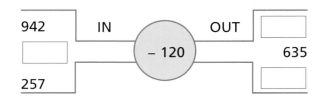

942	IN	OUT	
	− 120	635
257		

Test paper

1 Draw a ring around three numbers that are next to each other, which add up to 42.

1   2   3   4   5   6   7   8   9   10   11   12   13   14   15   16   17   18

2 Jo collects stickers. She has 220 stickers, and puts 30 stickers on each page of a book.

How many pages does she fill?

How many more stickers does she need to fill the next page?

Show your working.

3 Write in the missing number.

$\boxed{} \div 6 = 72$

Show your working.

4 This machine divides all numbers by 100.

IN — ÷ 100 — OUT

Complete this table.

IN	2500	2930	465			
OUT				38	8.9	0.35

Test paper

5 The formula for this number pattern is:

$\triangle = 3 \times \blacksquare - 1$

Write the missing numbers.

△	2				14
■	1	2	3	4	5

> If you don't know the answer to a question, go on to the next one. You can come back to the difficult questions at the end, if you have time.

6 Here are some number cards.

4   9   7   12   8   3

Use two of the cards to make a fraction equal to $\frac{1}{4}$ ⇒ ▭/▭

Use two different cards to make a fraction which is less than $\frac{1}{2}$ ⇒ ▭/▭

7 *n* stands for a number.

$n + 2 = 12$

What is the value of $n + 6$? ▭

8 Write these numbers in the correct places on the Venn Diagram:

17   210   27   48   216   72

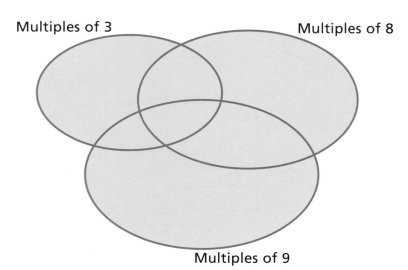

Multiples of 3   Multiples of 8

Multiples of 9

Marks

9 Five parcels weigh 76.5kg altogether.

If each parcel weighs the same, what will be the total weight of **three** of the parcels?

[　　　　] kg

Show your working.

10 Write these numbers in order of size, smallest first.

| 7.8 | 7.18 | 7.83 | 7.08 | 7.79 | 7.9 | 7.81 |

[　] [　] [　] [　] [　] [　] [　]

Smallest

11 Draw the lines of symmetry on these shapes.

 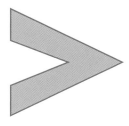 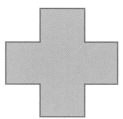

The line of symmetry is also called the mirror line. Imagine having a line with a mirror on it, so that the reflection makes the shape look whole again. A shape can have more than one mirror line.

Total

Test paper

Marks

12 The vertices of a shape have these co-ordinates.

(–3, 2)   (1, 2)   (1, –2)   (–3, –2)

Draw the shape on this grid.

What is the name of the shape?

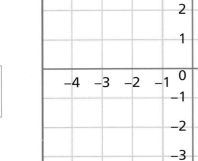

> Remember the first co-ordinate goes across and the second co-ordinate goes up or down.

13 Write the answer.

Work out the sums in brackets first.

(8 × 3) + (9 × 2) =

14 Find the numbers that are covered by the stars.

★84 × 37 = 2 5 3 ★ 8

Show your working.

Total

Marks

15 Two of these numbers can be divided by 3. Circle the two numbers.

     3103   **7418**   **1491**   **2093**   **4209**

16 These are the arm-spans of seven children in a class.

Name	Jo	Ahmed	Jack	Laura	Sam	Peter	James
Arm span (cm)	125	133	129	122	134	140	134

What is the median arm span in this group?   cm

Which children have the modal arm span?

What is the mean (average) arm span of this group?   cm

Show your working.

To find the mode, look for the number that occurs the most frequently. To find the median, put the numbers in order and find the middle number. To find the mean, work out the total and divide it by the number of items.

Total

Key facts 1

Multiplication table

×	1	2	3	4	5	6	7	8	9	10
1	1	2	3	4	5	6	7	8	9	10
2	2	4	6	8	10	12	14	16	18	20
3	3	6	9	12	15	18	21	24	27	30
4	4	8	12	16	20	24	28	32	36	40
5	5	10	15	20	25	30	35	40	45	50
6	6	12	18	24	30	36	42	48	54	60
7	7	14	21	28	35	42	49	56	63	70
8	8	16	24	32	40	48	56	64	72	80
9	9	18	27	36	45	54	63	72	81	90
10	10	20	30	40	50	60	70	80	90	100

Square, triangle and prime numbers to 100

Square numbers	1	4	9	16	25	36	49	64	81	100	121	144	169
Triangle numbers	1	3	6	10	15	21	28	36	45	55	66	78	91
Prime numbers	2	3	5	7	11	13	17	19	23	29	31	37	41
	43	47	53	59	61	67	71	73	79	83	89	97	

Averages

There are three types of average:

$$\text{mean} = \frac{\text{total number of items}}{\text{number of items used}}$$

median = the middle value when the numbers are ranged in order of size

mode = the number that occurs most often

Fractions, decimals and percentages

Fraction	$\frac{1}{2}$	$\frac{1}{4}$	$\frac{3}{4}$	$\frac{1}{5}$	$\frac{1}{10}$	$\frac{1}{8}$	$\frac{1}{3}$	$\frac{2}{3}$
Decimal	0.5	0.25	0.75	0.2	0.1	0.125	0.333	0.666
%	50%	25%	75%	20%	10%	$12\frac{1}{2}\%$	$33\frac{1}{3}\%$	$66\frac{2}{3}\%$

Key facts 2

3D shapes

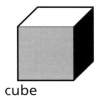 cube

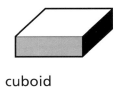 cuboid

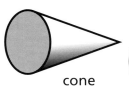 cylinder

 cone

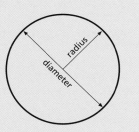 sphere

 triangular-based pyramid

2D shapes – circle facts

- the circumference is all the way round the circle
- a diameter is twice the radius.

Number of sides	3	4	5	6	7	8	9	10
Name of polygon	triangle	quadrilateral	pentagon	hexagon	heptagon	octagon	nonagon	decagon

Measurements

1000 g = 1 kg	10 mm = 1 cm	milli → thousandth	10 ml = 1 cl
1000 kg = 1 tonne	100 cm = 1 m	deci → tenth	10 cl = 1 dl
	1000 mm = 1 m	centi → hundredth	100 cl = 1 l
	1000 m = 1 km	kilo → thousand	100 ml = 1 dl
			1000 ml = 1 l

Time

24-hour time

Answers

page 6

1 a) 10, b) 100, c) 9600
2 a) 530   360
         149   531   64
   b) 97500   1800
         6.8   12.44   2.91
   c) 62   19   75
         2700   504   (level 5)
   d) 37   620   93.2
         7000   6800

page 7

1 210, 322, 420, 436, 565, 615
2 1046 < 10 046 > 4001 < 4621 < 24 660;
   412 000 > 264 000 > 62 040 > 6242 > 2640;
   197 824 > 19 999 > 2000 > 296 < 20 001;
   78 524 > 8578 < 57 788 < 527 282 > 57 822

page 8

1 520, 3670; 2600, 5300; 4, 16
2 100, 750; 0.5, 0.9; 100, 250
3 a) 950, b) 6100, c) 24, d) 4500

page 9

1 -3°C, -2°C
   10°C, -17°C
2 5°C, 6°C
   22°C, 8°C

page 10

1 a)$\frac{5}{10}$; b)$\frac{5}{6}$; c)$\frac{8}{12}$; d)$\frac{3}{4}$
2 a)$\frac{1}{3}$, $\frac{2}{6}$; b)$\frac{3}{4}$, $\frac{6}{8}$
3 a)$\frac{5}{15}$ b)$\frac{8}{24}$ c)$\frac{40}{50}$

page 11

1 $\frac{1}{2}$, $\frac{2}{3}$, $\frac{1}{4}$, $\frac{1}{3}$, $\frac{2}{5}$, $\frac{1}{2}$
2 $\frac{1}{2}$, $\frac{3}{5}$, $\frac{7}{10}$, $\frac{3}{4}$
3 b) (÷ 5) = $\frac{4}{15}$
4 $\frac{1}{8}$, $\frac{1}{6}$, $\frac{1}{5}$, $\frac{1}{3}$, $\frac{3}{8}$, $\frac{3}{6}$, $\frac{3}{5}$, $\frac{5}{8}$, $\frac{6}{8}$, $\frac{5}{6}$

page 12 (level 5)

1 a)$\frac{9}{8}$, b)$\frac{8}{5}$, c)$\frac{15}{2}$, d)$\frac{59}{10}$
2 b) $2\frac{2}{3}$, c) $2\frac{3}{4}$, d) $1\frac{7}{8}$
3 $\frac{18}{3}$, $\frac{12}{3}$, $\frac{30}{3}$, $\frac{21}{3}$; $\frac{72}{8}$, $\frac{16}{8}$, $\frac{24}{8}$, $\frac{40}{8}$
4 a)$\frac{9}{4}$, b)$\frac{11}{3}$, c) $2\frac{2}{9}$, d) $4\frac{3}{5}$, e) $1\frac{6}{7}$, f) $\frac{9}{2}$, g)$\frac{19}{8}$,
   h) $2\frac{5}{6}$

page 13

1 0.45, 0.03, 2.75, 4.7, 1.2, 5.75
2 $\frac{3}{10}$, $\frac{9}{100}$, $\frac{74}{100}$ ($\frac{37}{50}$), $\frac{25}{100}$ ($\frac{1}{4}$), $\frac{35}{100}$ ($\frac{7}{20}$),
   $\frac{6}{10}$ ($\frac{3}{5}$)
3

$\frac{1}{4}$	$\frac{7}{10}$	$2\frac{1}{2}$	$2\frac{1}{8}$	$1\frac{17}{50}$	$1\frac{3}{5}$	$3\frac{1}{5}$	$3\frac{47}{100}$	$1\frac{975}{1000}$
0.25	0.7	2.5	2.125	1.34	1.6	3.2	3.47	1.975

4 5 ÷ 8 = 0.625, 2 ÷ 5 = 0.4, 7 ÷ 9 = 0.7777777, this one is a recurring decimal, 4 ÷ 5 = 0.8

page 14

1 90%, 72%; 74%; 9 out of 10 was his best score
2 50%, 30%, 70%, 25%
3 a) 30%, b) 55%, c) 40%, d) 90%
4 a)$\frac{3}{5}$, b)$\frac{7}{20}$, c)$\frac{19}{20}$, d)$\frac{9}{50}$

page 15

1 60%, 0.75
2 0.1, 30%, 20%
3 0.6, 0.75, 0.32
4 40%, 33%, 8%, 85% (level 5)

page 16

1 a) 24, b) 100
2 375ml water, 125ml squash
3 £84
4 Cereal   Weight New weight (30% extra)
   Honeycrunch   370g   481g
   Choc Pops   400g   520g
   Crisp Flakes   280g   364g
   Bran Bites   420g   546g
   Oat Ovals   450g   585g   (level 5)

page 17

1 86 + 24, 84 + 26, 62 + 48, 42 + 68 (any three)

2 a) 15, b) 88, c) 64, d) 134

3

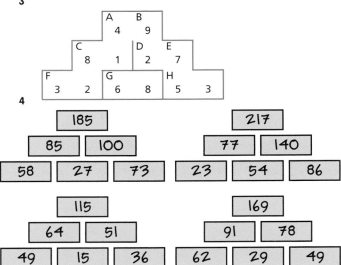

4

	185				217	
	85	100			77	140
58	27	73		23	54	86

	115				169	
	64	51			91	78
49	15	36		62	29	49

page 18

1 a) 434, b) 833, c) 598

2 125 and 170

3 a) 2, b) 8, b) 5

4 940cm, 1015cm

page 19

1 653

2 largest 5822, smallest 565

Flavour	Saturday	Sunday	Monday	Total
Vanilla	430	1655	2086	4171
Strawberry	592	1917	1775	4284
Chocolate	628	1893	2434	4955
Total	1650	5465	6295	

4 a) 902; b) 16 201; c) 94 067, d) 63 030

page 20

1 16.1 and 14.4

2 4

3 £173.90, £14.85, £239.50, £100

4 4.6 + 11.03 = 15.63; 57.8 + 2.95 = 60.75; 10.62 + 3.04 = 13.66

page 21

1 a) 22p; b) 32p

2 60 and 78; 78 and 22;
92 - 22 = 70, 92 - 60 = 32, 92 - 78 = 14, 92 - 85 = 7
greatest difference is with number 22, smallest difference
is with number 85

page 22

1 a) 190; b) 290

2 531 and 689

3 a) 820, 620; b) 367, 76; c) 302, 252

page 23

1 2762g

2

Across	Down
A 2639	A 2950
C 5401	B 3504
F 7107	D 8136
G 1685	E 1785

3 1444

page 24

1 a) £27.40; b) £66.55

2 23.8 and 10.2

3 Now   Mountain bike: £65.85   Shopper: £33.05
Saving   BMX bike: £13.9   Racer: £7.25

4 a) 5.32 – 1.85 = 3.47; b) 14.52 – 9.39 = 5.13;
c) 20.6 – 2.06 = 18.54

page 25

1 98 x 3

2 222g

3 a) 288g; b) 360g; c) 584g; d) 267g

page 26

1 1449, 3381
3864, 1932

2 1176, 620
4354, 1743
1984, 2430
1718, 2004

3 largest 742 x 8 = 5936, smallest 478 x 2 = 956

page 27 (level 5)

1 322m²

2 £1020

3 largest 632 x 9 = 5688, smallest 369 x 2 = 738

4 779 m², 1036m²

page 28

1 £21

2 4.8 kg

3 31.4

4 55, 56.5; 49, 46.9; 9, 7.8; 56, 59.6

5 (level 5)

out	32.2	27.3	89.6	3.5	112.7	4.9

out	8.56	20.32	42.88	55.8	0.24	28.36

page 29

1 23

2 26

3 16

4 a) 12 ÷ 4 = 3; b) 56 ÷ 7 = 8; c) 48 ÷ 3 = 16; d) 95 ÷ 5 = 19; e) 58 ÷ 2 = 29; f) 78 ÷ 6 = 13

5 82, 49

page 30

1 986

2 5 lengths, 5cm left over

3 7, 10, 36, 3

4 25 weeks

page 31 (level 5)

1 12

2 £162

3 821, 26

4 £13, £5.34, 90p, £1.30

page 32

1 105 ml

2 £3

3 252 pages

4 £1.40

5 £6.85, £8.05, 10 tickets with saving £17

page 33 (level 5)

1 4 weeks 5 days

2 15 miles, 20 miles

3 £106

page 34

1 300m

2 630mm; 1670mm or 1.67m, 1890mm

3 5

4 720g

page 35

1 1.2kg

2 a) 76; b) 1.5; c) 63; d) 6.8

3 a) 16 = 47, 59 = 90, 42 = 73, 45 = 76; b) 4.2 = 6.1; 5.9 = 7.8, 15.5 = 17.4; c) 27 = 8, 99 = 80, 33 = 14, 110 = 91; d) 6.7 = 2.6, 10 = 5.9, 12.6 = 8.5

page 36

1 a) 92; b) 10.6; c) 540; d) 18

2 a) 15; b) 20.9; c) 65; d) 401

3 a) 347g; b) 500g; c) 425g; d) 2.5kg; e) 52g; f) 2.58kg

page 37

1 3 years, 7 years, 46 years

2 a) 30; b) 12; c) 215; d) 271

4 Monday £1.50
Tuesday £2.95
Wednesday £3.40
Thursday £4.01
Friday £2.80

page 38

1 36 − 14 = 22, 14 + 22 = 36, 31 + 64 = 95, 95 - 64 = 31

2 a) 37 = 148, 91 = 364, 45 = 180; b) 315 = 550, 573 = 808, 497 = 732; c) 582 = 194, 177 = 59, 678 = 226; d) 942 = 822, 755 = 635, 257 =137

Test paper

Look in the margin at the marks boxes. Each box shows where one mark can be gained. Put in marks for correct answers and add them together for the final result.

1 13, 14, 15

2 7, 20

3 432

4

| in | 2500 | 2930 | 465 | 3800 | 890 | 35 |
| out | 25 | 29.3 | 4.65 | 38 | 8.9 | 0.35 |

5

| △ | 2 | 5 | 8 | 11 | 14 |
| ■ | 1 | 2 | 3 | 4 | 5 |

6 3/12; 4/9

7 16

8

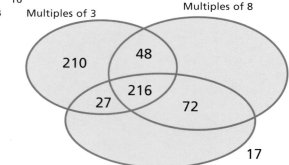

Multiples of 3 · Multiples of 8 · Multiples of 9

210 · 48 · 216 · 27 · 72 · 17

9 45.9kg

10 7.08, 7.18, 7.79, 7.8, 7.81, 7.83, 7.9

11

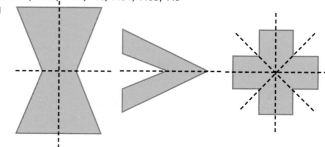

12 A square

13 42

14 684 x 37 = 25 308

15 1491, 4209

16 133cm, Sam and James, 131cm